SOLAR ECLIP

Richard P Holloway   MSc FBIS

Calculus Publishing

Eclipse data reproduced courtesy of Fred Espenak and Jay Anderson, NASA.

The publisher, author, and their respective employees or agents, shall not accept responsibility for injury, loss or damage incurred by any person acting or refraining from action as a result of this book whether or not such injury, loss or damage is in any way due to any negligent act or omission, breach of duty or default on the part of the publisher, author, or their respective employees or agents.

Published by Calculus Publishing, an imprint of Calculus International Limited
Beaumont House, 29 Beaumont Avenue, St Albans, AL1 4TL Tel: +44 (0)1727 854431
http://www.calculus-international.com/publishing/

Typeset by Calculus Publishing using Serif PagePlus 5.0 © 1997 Serif, Inc.

Pre-press by Colour Bytes, London.

Printed in the UK by L&S Printing Co. Ltd, Worthing.

Eclipse spectacles supplied by Peter Allen Eyeware, London.

Front cover photograph, the 1998 Venezuelan Solar Eclipse, by Cesar Briceno. (Taken using Kodachrome 64 slide film on a Celestron 6" Newtonian reflector, focal length 750mm, f/5, 1/2s exposure). Reproduced with kind permission of Cesar Briceno and the Harvard-Smithsonian Centre for Astrophysics.

ISBN 0 9535527 0 5

Acknowledgements

I have gathered information from a number of sources, but certainly the most important resource has been NASA and their excellent bulletin, The Total Solar Eclipse of 1999 August 11 (Espenak and Anderson, 1997). With their permission, several figures, tables and data and other information from the bulletin have been reproduced herein, either in original form or adapted, and in many cases simplified, to suit this publication.

I would also like to thank the following for their help, advice, and suggestions:

Yasmin Batliwala
Tim Acton
Paul Barwick
Barbara Barwick
Keith Clack of Beeches Display International
Ros of Colour Bytes
Tony Smith of L & S Printing Company

"It is not clear whether de Selby had heard of this [that winds have colours] but suggests (*Garcia, p 12*) that night, far from being caused by the commonly accepted theory of planetary movements, was due to accumulations of 'black air', produced by certain volcanic activities of which he does not treat in detail. See also p 79 and 945, *Country Album*. Le Fournier's comment (in *Homme ou Dieu*) is interesting. 'Un ne saura jamais jusqu'à quel point de Selby fut cause de la Grande Guerre, mais, sans aucun doute, ses théories excentriques - spécialement celle que nuit n'est pas un phénomène de nature, mais dans l'atmosphère un état malsain amené par un industrialisme cupide et sans pitié - auraient l'effet de produire un trouble profond dans les masses."

The Third Policeman, Flann O'Brien

Preface

I started looking for an eclipse guide for the forthcoming solar eclipse towards the end of 1998. I was looking for something for myself, and for my friends in Cornwall. A plethora of books exist on the subject in general, but I was unable to find a specific guide for the August 11th eclipse, suitable for the non-specialist. I decided that the best thing would be to write one myself.

I wanted to produce something for the complete beginner, someone with no knowledge of astronomy. Jargon, in the form of specialist astronomical terms has been almost completely eliminated and has only been used after explanation and where no other terms will do. At the end of the book, I have included a brief glossary.

To begin the book, I felt it necessary to introduce the subject of eclipses. I explain simply how they happen, followed by a short chapter describing the Sun, which I hope the reader will find interesting.

The main objective of the book is to maximise the reader's chance of seeing the eclipse and getting the most out of the event by understanding what to expect. Most of the remainder of the book is geared towards this aim. I discuss the path and timings for the eclipse in mainland Britain and northern France, give places and times of the eclipse, as well as the likely outcome of the weather. For the more adventurous reader, I have included a chapter on observing the eclipse abroad, and where the best places are.

I explain how to observe the eclipse safely, what to expect, what the various phenomena are, and when they happen. There is an important chapter on how to photograph and videorecord the eclipse.

The text is supported by a comprehensive set of diagrams and tabulated information, to aid understanding and to provide essential data in a simple form.

There has been a lot of hype in the media about this year's eclipse. I heard recently that about 2 million people are set to descend upon Cornwall during eclipse week in August this year, and stories of how people are renting out their homes for several thousand pounds for the week. Quite why such an event as this has caught the public imagination is hard to say. In astronomical terms, total solar eclipses are not rare occurrences, about every 18 months, with partial eclipses once every 4 months or so. That one should occur in the United Kingdom, is a rare event - the last total eclipse in Britain was in 1927. Nonetheless, it would hard to justify spending so much money to go to Cornwall, when you could spend the same, or less, and go somewhere certainly more exotic and where the weather will be more reliable. That said, I'll be going, but it won't cost me the Earth because my sister lives there.

Wherever you decide to be on August 11th 1999, protect your eyesight, and have fun - it should be awesome !

Richard P Holloway MSc FBIS FRAS

Vinça, France   January 1999

Contents

List of figures

List of tables

Safety warning

Most individuals who sustain eclipse-related eye injuries are children and young adults. Never observe the Sun without taking proper precautions - failure to take correct protective measures can result in serious eye damage and blindness.

Eclipse viewing spectacles

The viewing spectacles supplied free with this book can be used to view the eclipse directly during the partial eclipse phases. Please follow the instructions printed on them. They need not be used during the total eclipse stage.

Additional pairs of eclipse viewing spectacles can be purchased at the special price of £1.50 (normally £2.00) direct from Calculus Publishing.

To obtain additional pairs send a cheque/P.O. made payable to 'Calculus International Limited' to:

Calculus Publishing
Beaumont House
29 Beaumont Avenue
St Albans
AL1 4TL

Introduction to solar eclipses

The last total solar eclipse in Britain was in 1927. After August 11th 1999, the next total solar eclipse in Britain will be in 2090.

The earliest record of a solar eclipse is probably that which occurred in China in 2136 BC. In Britain, the first recorded eclipse was in 538 AD, and is described in the Anglo-Saxon Chronicle. The last total solar eclipse to have occurred in Britain was on 29th June 1927. Totality occurred over the north of England and lasted for about half a minute, though observing conditions were generally poor.

Today, there is a great deal of interest in solar eclipses and thousands of astronomers travel the world to observe and photograph the phenomenon, wherever and whenever it occurs. For the observer in Britain who wants to stay closer to home, August 11th 1999 offers the potential to witness one of the most fascinating of astronomical events. But beware - if you miss it, for most of us there won't be a second chance. If you stay in Britain you'll have to wait until 23rd September 2090.

Before getting into the details of where the eclipse will occur and where the best place to be is, let's look at the basics. I begin with a brief description of the different types of solar eclipse and consider the science of eclipse watching.

So what is a solar eclipse? It is surprising that people often get confused by this, but it really is very straightforward. It is when the Moon moves between the Sun and the Earth so that a shadow is projected onto the Earth.

There are three basic types of solar eclipse; *total, partial* and *annular*. A total solar eclipse is seen when the Sun's disk is completely obscured by the moon. A partial eclipse is when only part of the Sun's disk is hidden.

Figure 1, shows how a total eclipse will be seen by an observer located within the *umbra* of the shadow. A partial eclipse will be seen by an observer located within the *penumbra*. Umbra is the region on the Earth where the Sun is completely hidden by the Moon. In the penumbra, the Sun is only partly obscured.

Figure 1. Total and partial solar eclipse (not to scale)

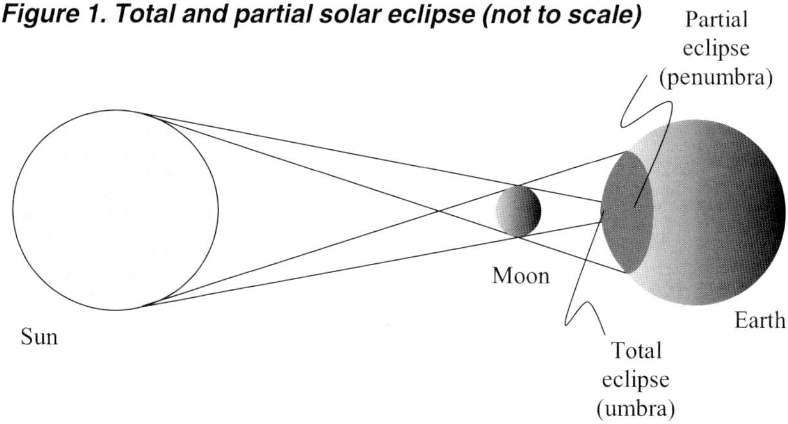

Partial eclipse (penumbra)

Sun

Moon

Earth

Total eclipse (umbra)

Variations in the distance between the Moon and the Earth are brought about because of the slightly non-circular orbit of the Moon around the Earth. If this distance increases, the Moon will appear to be slightly smaller than the Sun in the sky. Under these conditions, when the Moon passes directly in front of the Sun, as seen from the Earth, the region of totality will lie some distance above the Earth's surface, observed as an annular eclipse, as shown in Figure 2 overleaf.

There is another type of solar eclipse, known as *annular-total,* where an annular eclipse briefly changes to a total eclipse. These are very rare indeed.

Figure 2. Annular solar eclipse

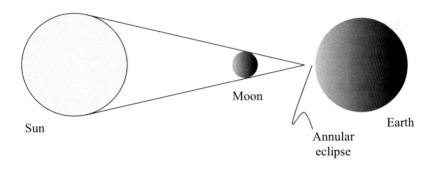

Sun

Moon

Earth

Annular
eclipse

So how do the different eclipses vary in what they look like from the Earth? During a partial eclipse, the Sun is only partly obscured by the Moon, as seen from Earth - figure 3.

Figure 3. Partial solar eclipse

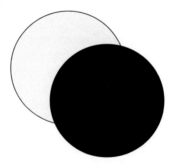

During totality, the Sun's bright disk is completely obscured by the Moon, surrounded by the pearly white glow of the *corona*, the Sun's outermost atmosphere - figure 4.

Figure 4. Total solar eclipse

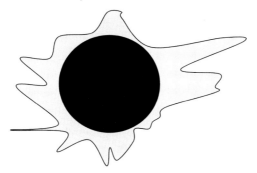

An annular eclipse appears as a bright ring, or annulus, surrounding the Moon - figure 5.

Figure 5. Annular eclipse

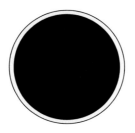

Astronomers, amateur and professional, have an armoury of seemingly impenetrable jargon. This is kept to a minimum throughout this book. However, for the purposes of timings it is worth becoming familiar with the terms *first, second, third* and *fourth contact*. These will be used later in the book.

- First contact   - partial eclipse begins

- Second contact   - total (or annular) eclipse begins

- Third contact   - total (or annular) eclipse ends

- Fourth contact   - partial eclipse ends

Why we are so interested in observing eclipses? That a solar eclipse is a spectacular and amazing sight to behold is reason enough to observe it, but it is also a great opportunity to harness a natural phenomenon to illustrate some basic scientific principles. For example, the event can be used to demonstrate the application of Newton's laws of motion, to stimulate interest in technology through the use of optical devices, such as pinhole cameras, telescopes and binoculars, and to learn about the Sun.

Astronomers are interested in total eclipses because they provide us with a rare glimpse of the Sun's surroundings, the *prominences*, *chromosphere* and the Sun's outer atmosphere, the *corona*. I talk about the Sun in more detail in the following chapter.

The Sun, our star

The Sun is 150,000,000 kilometres away - light from the Sun takes over 8 minutes to reach the Earth.

The Sun is our nearest star, and one of about 100,000,000,000 stars in our galaxy, the Milky Way. (Astronomers refer to the Sun as a rather ordinary yellow dwarf star of spectral type G2V.) Because of its relative proximity, at about 150 million kilometres away (93 million miles) it is also our best studied star.

To get a better idea of distance, astronomers use the speed of light as a measure. Light travels at about 300,000 kilometres every second (186,000 miles/second). This means that light from the Sun takes about 8 minutes to reach us. You could say that the Sun is 8 light minutes away. By comparison, the light from the next nearest star, Proxima Centauri, takes about 4.2 light years to reach us. In other words, it is 4.2 light years away. It is interesting to note that if we were to set off for Proxima Centauri in a spacecraft travelling at a tenth of the speed of light it would take 42 years to get there. Current spacecraft technology allows for speeds much less than this. For example, the *Mars Polar Lander* is currently on its way to Mars at a speed of 1.7 kilometres/second. At this speed, it would take around 750,000 years to reach Proxima Centauri - not a practical proposition.

When we look at the Sun we see its most visible surface layer, the brilliant yellow *photosphere*, where the temperature is around 5,500 degrees (iron melts at about 1,500 degrees). Above this 300 km thick layer, the temperature gradually falls to about 4,000 degrees before starting to climb again at the base of a layer called the *chromosphere*. The temperature gradually rises through the chromosphere reaching a temperature of 10,000 degrees until reaching a region called the *transition zone*. Here the temperature increases rapidly, through a layer of gas only 200 km thick, quickly reaching over 1,000,000 degrees. Moving further out we enter the Sun's outermost atmosphere, the corona, a tenuous gas stretching millions of kilometres out into space.

Figure 6. The Sun's atmosphere

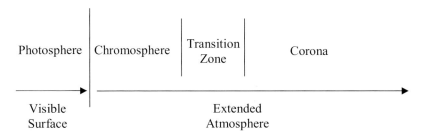

The chromosphere and corona, that make up the Sun's outer atmosphere, are not normally apparent to the observer without special equipment. During a total solar eclipse they reveal themselves because the much brighter photosphere is obscured. At totality, the corona becomes visible as a pearly, subtly structured, halo of light. For a few seconds before and after totality, the chromosphere briefly flashes into view as a pinkish rim surrounding the Sun. Its striking colour prompted early observers to name it chromosphere, from the Greek *khroma* (colour) + *sphaira* (sphere).

The Sun is a nuclear reactor on a grand scale. The enormous temperatures and pressures at the centre of the Sun ignite nuclear fusion reactions that convert hydrogen into helium. This process releases a vast amount of energy. The rate of energy release is roughly equivalent to a staggering 4,000,000,000,000,000,000,000,000 domestic 100 Watt light bulbs!

The energy generated by these reactions is not liberated immediately. It takes a while to diffuse and convect to the Sun's surface. In fact, the energy being produced at the centre of the Sun as you read this, will not be seen brightening someone's day for another 10 million years - assuming we humans are still here, of course.

The thermonuclear engine in the Sun's interior ignited 4,500 million years ago when the solar system began. Today, 71% of the Sun's volume is hydrogen, 27% helium, and the remaining 2% is composed of other elements. With hydrogen as the main fuel for the engine, there is still plenty in the tank, and enough to keep the Sun shining for another 4,500 million years before we see any major changes. However, the Sun will not go on forever. Like all stars it will eventually die.

Table 1. Basic solar data

Mass	2×10^{30} kg (3.33×10^5 Earth masses)
Diameter	1.4×10^6 km
Volume	1.4×10^{27} m^3 (1.3×10^6 Earth volumes)
Gravity	273.87 ms^{-2} ($27.94 \times$ Earth gravity)
Total radiation	3.83×10^{26} Watts
Distance to Earth	1.496×10^{11} m
Surface temperature	5770 Kelvin
Central temperature	15×10^6 Kelvin

The eclipse of 1999
in Britain and France

On August 11th 1999, the total solar eclipse will begin at 11:10 British Summer Time in the Scilly Isles and will finish in mainland Britain 4 minutes later.

The perpetual voyage of the Moon's umbral shadow through space will be interrupted briefly when it strikes the Earth in the north west Atlantic Ocean near Nova Scotia at 09:30:57 GMT on 11th August 1999. It will then travel some 14,000 km across the Earth's surface on a journey that will take it over the Atlantic Ocean, the south-west British Isles, central Europe, the Middle East, Pakistan and India before leaving the Earth, just 3 hours and 7 minutes later.

The first major landfall for the path of totality will be the Isles of Scilly at 11:09 British Summer Time (BST), reaching the Cornish coast one minute later. All hopes will be pinned on the weather! Assuming that fortune favours south-west Britain with clear skies, a total eclipse will be observed in a substantial proportion of Cornwall and parts of Devon.

During a solar eclipse, the period of totality is longest along a path drawn by the centre of the Moon's shadow. This is known as the centre line. In Cornwall, the centre line runs from the western Cornish coast near St. Just, through a point north of Penzance (11:10 BST) eastwards through Falmouth (11:11) - see figure 7. Observers situated along this line will experience totality for just over 2 minutes, the maximum period in mainland Britain.

The northern limit of totality lies along a path running from the western Cornish coast at Port Quin Bay, northwest of Wadebridge, through Newton Abbot (11:14) in the east and the Devon coast at Babbacombe Bay. Plymouth (11:12) is north of the centre line but will experience over 1.5 minutes of totality.

Figure 7. Eclipse path in Britain

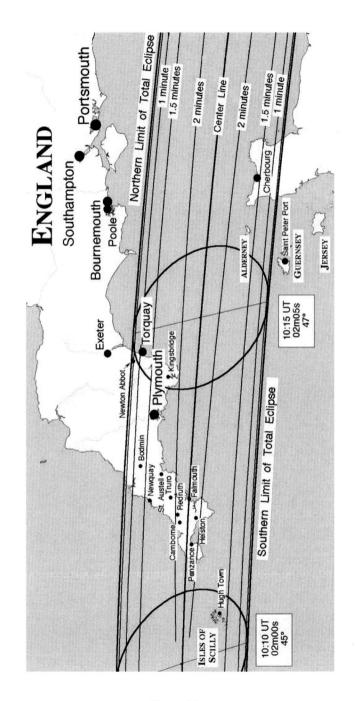

Table 2. Eclipse times in Britain
(in BST)

Location	1st Contact Partial Eclipse Begins	2nd Contact Total Eclipse Begins	3rd Contact Total Eclipse Ends	4th Contact Partial Eclipse Ends	Maximum Totality	Length of Totality
Bodmin	9:57:51	11:12:22	11:13:41	12:33:00	11:13:01	1m 19s
Camborne	9:56:58	11:11:02	11:13:03	12:32:03	11:12:02	2m 01s
Falmouth	9:57:08	11:11:19	11:13:22	12:32:28	11:12:20	2m 02s
Helston	9:56:54	11:11:02	11:13:03	12:32:09	11:12:02	2m 01s
Hugh Town	9:55:45	11:09:43	11:11:24	12:30:30	11:10:33	1m 41s
Kingsbridge	9:58.35	11.13.18	11.15.10	12:34:34	11:14:14	1m 52s
Newquay	9:57:25	11:11:40	11:13:18	12:32:25	11:12:29	1m 38s
Newton Abbot	9:59:00	11:14:21	11:14:50	12:34:47	11:14:35	0m 30s
Penzance	9:56:39	11:10:39	11:12:41	12:31:41	11:11:40	2m 02s
Plymouth	9:58:17	11:12:54	11:14:33	12:33:54	11:13:43	1m 39s
Redruth	9:57:04	11:11:09	11:13:10	12:32:11	11:12:10	2m 01s
Saint Austell	9:57:36	11:11:54	11:13:44	12:32:53	11:12:49	1m 50s
Saltash	9:58:16	11:12:53	11:14:29	12:33:51	11:13:41	1m 35s
Torquay	9:59:02	11:14:08	11:15:15	12:34:58	11:14:42	1m 07s
Truro	9:57:18	11:11:28	11:13:25	12:32:29	11:12:27	1m 57s

From Torquay, at 11:14 am BST, the shadow will head out across the English Channel. The centre line passes north of the Channel Isles, though Alderney (11:15) will find itself well inside the region of totality for about 1.5 minutes. Guernsey and Jersey are a little too far south to experience totality. Minutes later, the next landfall for the Moon's shadow will be the Cherbourg peninsula in northern France. After, it will race across central Europe towards the Middle East and Asia. As you can see from the timings above, the eclipse moves quickly across the Earth's surface, at speeds approaching 1 km/second (or 2250 miles per hour).

Eclipse watchers who have travelled to northern France will have increased their chances of success, in that they may be able to move to more favourable locations *ahead of the eclipse*, should weather forecasts be unfavourable for their locale. The centre line first reaches France on the Normandy coast near to Fécamp at 12:20 local time (BST+1). Totality in northern France touches the major towns of Le Havre (12:19), Dieppe (12:21), Rouen (12:21), Amiens (12:23) and Reims (12:25), which all enjoy 1.5 - 2 minutes of totality. Progressing towards Germany, the northern path of totality passes through southern Belgium and Luxembourg, while in France, Metz (12:29) is close to the centre line and Strasbourg (12:31) is south of the centre line. The path for this region and timings are given below.

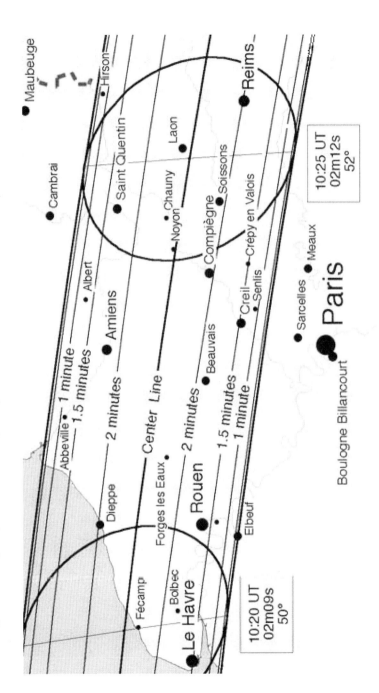

Figure 8. Eclipse path in France (west)

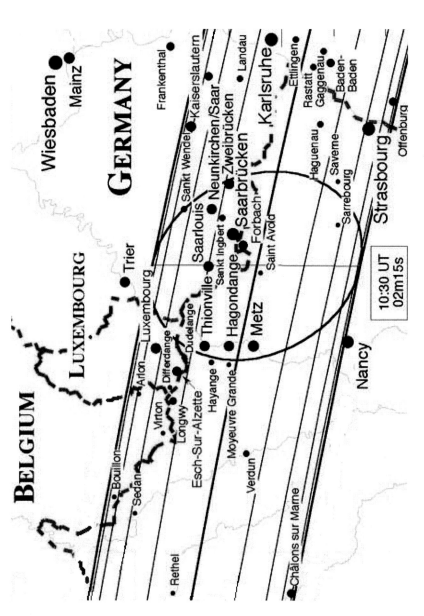

Figure 9. Eclipse path in France (east)

Table 3. Eclipse times in France
in local time (BST+1)

Location	1st Contact Partial Eclipse Begins	2nd Contact Total Eclipse Begins	3rd Contact Total Eclipse Ends	4th Contact Partial Eclipse Ends	Maximum Totality	Length of Totality
Abbeville	11:04:31	12:21:45	12:22:55	13:43:48	12:22:20	1m 10s
Albert	11:05:25	12:22:54	12:24:13	13:45:12	12:23:34	1m 19s
Amiens	11:04:55	12:22:04	12:23:56	13:44:40	12:23:00	1m 51s
Beauvais	11:04:16	12:21:36	12:23:31	13:44:32	12:22:33	1m 54s
Bolbec	11:02:30	12:19:12	12:21:03	13:41:48	12:20:08	1m 51s
Châlons sur Mar	11:06:45	12:25:50	12:26:22	13:48:40	12:26:06	0m 33s
Charleville Méz	11:07:47	12:26:03	12:27:27	13:48:44	12:26:45	1m 24s
Chauny	11:05:48	12:23:17	12:25:27	13:46:21	12:24:22	2m 10s
Cherbourg	11:00:11	12:16:11	12:17:45	13:38:11	12:16:58	1m 35s
Compiàgne	11:05:10	12:22:42	12:24:45	13:45:49	12:23:43	2m 02s
Creil	11:04:38	12:22:25	12:23:52	13:45:18	12:23:09	1m 27s
Crépy en Valois	11:05:07	12:23:02	12:24:33	13:46:01	12:23:48	1m 31s
Dieppe	11:03:30	12:20:09	12:22:10	13:42:39	12:21:09	2m 01s
Fécamp	11:02:31	12:18:57	12:21:05	13:41:32	12:20:01	2m 07s
Forbach	11:10:14	12:29:08	12:31:21	13:52:46	12:30:14	2m 13s
Forges les Eaux	11:03:47	12:20:43	12:22:50	13:43:34	12:21:47	2m 07s
Hagondange	11:09:18	12:27:56	12:30:09	13:51:30	12:29:02	2m 14s
Haguenau	11:11:13	12:30:38	12:32:48	13:54:32	12:31:43	2m 09s
Hayange	11:09:12	12:27:46	12:29:56	13:51:15	12:28:51	2m 10s
Hirson	11:07:06	12:25:23	12:26:10	13:47:36	12:25:46	0m 48s
Le Havre	11:02:03	12:18:49	12:20:20	13:41:14	12:19:35	1m 31s
Longwy	11:08:57	12:27:28	12:29:21	13:50:39	12:28:24	1m 53s
Metz	11:09:13	12:27:56	12:30:09	13:51:35	12:29:02	2m 13s
Moyeuvre Grande	11:09:07	12:27:42	12:29:56	13:51:17	12:28:49	2m 14s
Noyon	11:05:30	12:22:55	12:25:07	13:46:00	12:24:01	2m 11s
Reims	11:06:32	12:24:36	12:26:36	13:47:56	12:25:36	1m 59s
Rethel	11:07:09	12:25:05	12:27:15	13:48:19	12:26:10	2m 10s
Rouen	11:03:06	12:20:11	12:21:51	13:42:51	12:21:01	1m 40s
Saint Avold	11:09:55	12:28:47	12:31:02	13:52:30	12:29:55	2m 15s
Saint Quentin	11:06:03	12:23:39	12:25:22	13:46:19	12:24:31	1m 43s
Sarrebourg	11:10:10	12:29:41	12:31:19	13:53:22	12:30:30	1m 38s
Saverne	11:10:36	12:30:07	12:31:56	13:53:54	12:31:02	1m 49s
Sedan	11:08:02	12:26:19	12:27:54	13:49:10	12:27:07	1m 35s
Senlis	11:04:42	12:22:44	12:23:51	13:45:30	12:23:17	1m 07s
Soissons	11:05:45	12:23:29	12:25:32	13:46:41	12:24:30	2m 03s
Strasbourg	11:11:03	12:30:58	12:32:29	13:54:40	12:31:41	1m 01s
Thionville	11:09:23	12:27:59	12:30:06	13:51:25	12:29:03	2m 07s
Verdun	11:08:13	12:26:42	12:28:50	13:50:15	12:27:46	2m 09s

The English weather

This subject will be on the mind of all eclipse goers in the weeks and days leading up to the event. We will all be hoping for clear skies, but realistically what is the weather likely to throw at us?

Statistics from ground and satellite based observations of the weather in August indicates average cloud cover over Cornwall of around 60%. On average, August in Cornwall has about 6 days with clear skies and little cloud cover. Another significant factor in assessing the chance of seeing the eclipse, is the height of the Sun in the sky. The lower the Sun, the greater the chance that cloud cover will interfere with the view, since more of the Earth's atmosphere will lie in the line of sight between observer and Sun. In Britain, it will be mid morning with the Sun about 45 degrees in the sky.

Adding up all these factors gives us roughly a 45% chance of seeing the eclipse. While this may not sound encouraging, we can take heart that the eclipse is located in one of the sunniest summer locations in the British Isles. We can improve our chances by keeping an eye on the weather forecast and selecting the most promising observing location based on the latest information available.

In Britain, the climate is dominated by weather systems moving in from the Atlantic Ocean. Usually this gives us warm summers and mild winters, but brings with it generally damp conditions. The alternating stream of incoming high and low pressure systems (also called anticyclones and cyclones) contributes to the inherently changeable nature of the British weather.

On eclipse day we will be hoping that a high pressure system will be firmly in place over England. Under these conditions we are most likely to get dry sunny weather. Should a low pressure system persist instead, we will most likely see damp overcast weather. Statistically, we have about a one third chance of changeable conditions, a one third chance of a persistent low pressure system, and a one third chance of what we want, a persistent high pressure system.

Other conditions to watch out for are cold fronts. These can lead to unstable weather, and cloud cover. At these times coastal effects can be significant, since sea breezes often reduce the onset of this type of cloud formation. Under these conditions, head for the beach. On the other hand, if the weather is being dominated by a southerly wind, low cloud can be produced as the incoming warm humid air is cooled by the English Channel. Under these conditions, the best advice is to head inland, north-east towards Bodmin.

The best chance lies in watching the weather forecasts closely.

What happens during an eclipse

An eclipse is more than daytime darkness - look out for these phenomena...

I have considered the basics of eclipses, the nature of the Sun, and where and when the eclipse will happen. Wherever you decide to observe the eclipse you need to be prepared. In this chapter I describe what happens during an eclipse, what you can expect to see, and when.

I have already introduced the terms *first, second, third* and *fourth contact.* We now use these to describe a typical sequence of events and describe some of the effects during the eclipse.

In the previous chapter I looked at the path of the eclipse and gave examples of approximate times of maximum eclipse. Taking Plymouth as an example, from Table 2, the timings (in BST) for *first, second, third* and *fourth contact,* will be:

09:58:17	First contact - partial eclipse begins
11:12:54	Second contact - total eclipse begins
11:13:43	Moment of maximum eclipse
11:14:33	Third contact - total eclipse ends
12:33:54	Fourth contact - partial eclipse ends

We can see that from the time of first contact to total eclipse is about an hour and a quarter, and a similar time will elapse after totality before the Moon no longer covers any part of the Sun. The period of totality is from second contact to third contact, which, in our example, lasts for over one and a half minutes.

What can we actually expect to see before, during and after totality? You may have already heard of the so called *diamond ring* effect, and we discussed in an earlier chapter the chromosphere and corona. I describe below the phenomena that we can expect to see and when they will occur.

As totality approaches, the thin crescent of the Sun begins to disappear. At this point an effect called *Baily's beads* can be seen for a few seconds. The Sun's waning crescent appears as a string of bright points, or beads, as the light becomes broken up by the irregular surface of the Moon. Shafts of light are seen shining through the valleys on the Moon's surface. The effect is named after the English astronomer Francis Baily (1774-1844) who observed it during the solar eclipse of 1836. As these beads disappear, the last bead will sparkle and shine like a jewel, in the so called *diamond ring* effect. This will be visible for perhaps 3 or 4 seconds, before the Sun becomes completely obscured, and the solar chromosphere flashes into view, as a reddish/pinkish rim around the Moon's disk. It will last only a few seconds before giving way to the pearly glow of the corona. Solar *prominences* may also be visible for a little longer than the chromosphere. This will depend on how active the Sun is on the day.

During totality, the sky will become as dark as it is during the normal evening twilight, possibly darker. Looking around, you will be able to see the pinkish glow of the horizon, in semi-darkness because you will be looking into areas where a partial eclipse is still in progress. It will appear as if sunset is occurring all around you. As totality ends, you will get another chance to see these effects again, in reverse order.

Another interesting phenomenon is an effect called *shadow bands*. In the minutes before and after totality, narrow shadows 4-6 inches wide and about three feet apart may be seen moving quickly across light surfaces on the ground, rather like when ripples are seen in reflection off the surface of water. This happens because of a lensing effect caused by the Earth's upper atmosphere. This bends and focuses the light from the Sun's thin crescent onto the Earth. Shadow bands need a very clear sky to occur, and then can be seen more easily by laying a white sheet over the ground.

In summary, the sequence of events will be:

* First contact (partial eclipse begins)
* Shadow bands
* Baily's beads
* Diamond ring
* Second contact (totality begins)
* Chromosphere flashes into view
* Chromosphere no longer visible, dominant feature is corona
* Chromosphere flashes into view again
* Third contact (totality ends)
* Diamond ring
* Baily's beads
* Shadow bands
* Fourth contact (partial eclipse ends)

Most of the action occurs shortly before, during and just after totality, a period spanning a few minutes. Clearly, you need to remain alert, especially if you're planning to photograph these effects.

Figure 10. The English sky at totality

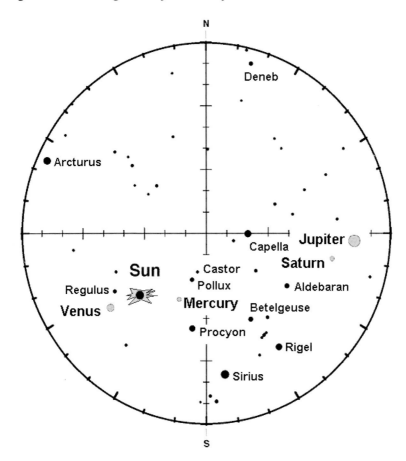

Provided you are not in a built-up area where street lights will illuminate the sky, during totality you should be able to identify a number of bright stars and planets. Venus will be clearly visible. Mercury will be much fainter but still discernible close to the Sun. The winter constellations should be visible, especially the bright stars Capella, Aldebaran, Procyon, Betelgeuse and Sirius. Good night-vision is a problem during an eclipse because the eye does not have time to adjust properly in the short space of time. To overcome this, some eclipse watchers even cover one eye with an eye-patch about 10 minutes before totality, and remove it when totality begins.

How to observe the eclipse safely

Most eclipse related eye injuries occur in children and young adults.

I now describe how to observe the eclipse, and how to do it safely. Safety relating to eclipse watching is a well worn theme, but is important - failure to use proper observing methods can result in permanent and severe damage to eyesight. During the months and weeks approaching the eclipse, there will be a lot of information, and misinformation, about observing the eclipse. Unfortunately, many people will be put off watching the eclipse at all, while others will sadly injure their eyes observing without due care. Both these outcomes can be avoided by following simple guidelines.

Many people are aware that they should not look at the Sun through a telescope, camera, binoculars, or similar optical instruments, without the protection of special filters. It is less well known that you can cause severe and permanent damage to your eyesight just by looking up at the Sun directly with the naked eye. Even the thin crescent that remains when 99% of the Sun is obscured by the Moon is bright enough to cause eye injury when observed with the naked eye. The potential for injury is increased because this type of injury, known as retinal burn or eclipse blindness, is not accompanied by any pain as the injury occurs. This may be the reason that most individuals who sustain eclipse-related eye injuries are children and young adults.

Remember that the only safe time to look at the Sun without suitable protection is during the period of totality, when the Sun is completely obscured by the Moon. You must protect your eyes throughout all other times, including during the partial phases of the eclipse, with filters designed specifically for eclipse watching. Only during the brief phase of totality should you remove these filters, as they will only impair your view, and observe the eclipse directly. Please note, however, that before the Sun emerges from behind the Moon you must either look away, or protect your eyes again.

The safest filters to use are those specifically designed for the purpose of observing the Sun, such as those provided free with this book. Unsafe filters include sunglasses, smoked glass, CDs, floppy disks, and most types of developed film. Some experienced eclipse watchers use specially developed black and white film. Do not attempt this unless you are very familiar with the technique as only specific types of film are suitable.

Filters for eye protection usually come in the form of spectacles, often with 'lenses' made of *aluminised Mylar*. Ensure that the ones you intend to use are sound, that they are not damaged or scratched, as this can impair their effectiveness, and that they carry suitable standards marks such as the CE mark or BSI kite mark. Any old filter will not do! Note that eclipse spectacles are **not** suitable for use in optical instruments such as telescopes, binoculars and cameras.

If you suffer from any eye impediment, disease, cataracts or have had eye surgery you should seek specialist medical advice before observing.

You can avoid looking at the Sun at all during the partial phases by piercing a small hole in a piece of card and allowing sunlight to pass through the hole onto a second piece of smooth white card supported a few feet behind. The image will not be very large, but will allow you to see the partial phases in complete safety without the need for special filters.

For telescopes, cameras, etc., a special filter will need to be used to cover the full aperture of the instrument. The types of filter that fit over the eyepiece of telescopes are not recommended, as these can crack because of the intense heat created. Filters supplied for telescopes are usually made of a metallised film that fits over the instrument aperture. For example, *Baader Astrosolar® Safety Film*, comes in A4 sheets and can be cut and fitted as required (about £10.00 per sheet). For suppliers, refer to classified advertisements in popular astronomy magazines, or contact David Hinds Ltd (01442 827768) who also stock a range of telescopes, other filters and accessories.

If you have any doubts, then by far the safest method is to project an image from the telescope onto a piece of smooth white card supported a few feet behind the telescope eyepiece. You can focus the image using the telescope eyepiece and avoid having to look at the Sun directly. It also has the advantage of allowing several observers to see the image at the same time. Take care though, and remember not to look through the eyepiece, and make sure nobody else does if it's left unattended.

It is a good idea to try these techniques out beforehand, so that you are well versed with the procedures on the day. In the next chapter I describe how you can photograph and even videotape the eclipse.

Photographing and videotaping

The first successful photograph of a solar eclipse, showing the corona and prominences, was taken by Berkowski on 28 July 1851, with an exposure time of 24s, using the 6.25 inch Koenigsberg heliometer.

There are several books devoted entirely to astrophotography. This chapter is designed to give you the basics, and allow you to get very impressive results. Eclipse photography is surprisingly easy and videotaping is even easier, if you follow these guidelines.

Photography

A single-lens reflex (SLR) camera, equipped with a telephoto lens, cable shutter release, tripod, and an appropriate filter will do. Another setup favoured by eclipse photographers is to connect your camera to a telescope using a technique known as *afocal coupling.* (Personally, I use the latter technique employing an SLR camera with the lens removed and linked via a T-peice and bayonet connector to the eyepiece of my telescope, a 4.5" catadioptric reflector.) If you have an SLR camera and a telescope, then visit your nearest specialist camera shop who should be able to advise you and sell you the appropriate connectors for your own telescope and camera, provided they are standard sizes.

If you don't have a telescope, this doesn't matter. However, a standard 50mm lens will produce a very small image of the eclipse on a 35mm film. You'll need to use a longer focal length lens, preferably at least 300mm. Ideally, go for a 500mm lens. It will render a good size image on your film. As a rule of thumb, dividing the focal length by 100 will give you the approximate image size on the film, e.g. a 500mm lens will produce an image size of approximately 5mm on 35mm film. Remember that the solar corona can stretch out from the Sun for several solar radii, so as you increase the image size on the film using bigger lenses, you increase the risk of losing the corona off the edge of the film.

Whichever setup you use you will need a protective filter for the front of your camera or telescope lens. *These need to be specified as safe for solar photography*, and usually take the form of a metallised film. The term often used is "neutral-density filter", for which you will need to consult your local camera shop or specialist suppliers (note that the Wratten type photographic filters are not safe for the eye).

A grading system is used to describe the level by which they reduce the intensity of light. An ND 5 reduces the intensity by a factor of 100,000 (5 zeroes), whereas an ND 4 reduces the intensity by a factor of 10,000 (4 zeroes) and so on. ND 5 is a good choice for eclipse photography. Again, *Baader Astrosolar® Safety Film* can be used and is equivalent to ND 5 in light reduction. The metallised ND filters give a whitish image of the Sun. If you prefer a redder sun, you can add a red or orange filter.

A fine grain film can be used, such as ISO (ASA) 100 or less, as this will give you a better quality image than a fast film. Kodachrome 64 (ISO/ASA 64) is a good choice.

Exposure times can be difficult to gauge, since this depends on the brightness of the image. This, in turn, depends on the particular effect being photographed, the clarity of the sky, the height of the Sun in the sky and the grade of filter used. To improve your chances of a good picture, always shoot with a range of speeds (a technique known as *bracketing*). If you have an autowind feature on your camera, it should improve your chances of taking a range of speeds. I give suggested shutter speeds for the various eclipse features, based on using an ND 5 filter, ISO/ASA 50 and 100 film, and the f/8 stop on your camera.

Before you start, FIT YOUR FILTER. Focus your camera on infinity, disable the flash, and ensure that that the automatic exposure is switched off so you have full manual control of shutter speed. Between shoots, cover your camera lens with a black cloth. This will prevent overheating and the eliminate the potential for camera damage.

The following exposure times are a guide - always take a number of exposures around the quoted figure below.

Table 4. Exposure times guide (using f/8)

With Filter		ISO/ASA 50	ISO/ASA 100
Partial Eclipse	(see note 1)	1/250	1/500
Baily's Beads	(see note 2)	1/1000	1/2000
Without Filter			
Diamond Ring	(see note 3)	1/30	1/60
Chromosphere		1/1000	1/2000
Prominences		1/500	1/1000
Inner Corona	(see note 4)	1/125	1/250
Outer Corona	(see note 4)	1/2 s - 8 s	

Notes

1. It is a good idea to take your last partial eclipse shots about 10 minutes before totality and put a fresh roll of film in your camera.

2. Baily's Bead's are highly variable in brightness. The exposure times above are not definitive - take as many bracketed exposures as you can. Afterwards, remove the filter for the diamond ring effect, but don't look through the viewfinder.

3. Immediately after the diamond ring disappears, take as many bracketed shots as possible to capture the chromosphere and prominences.

4. Vary shutter speeds from 1/125 up to 8 seconds. The longer the shutter speed, the greater the extent of the corona that will be imaged, bearing in mind that the corona gets fainter with distance from the Sun. The price for the longer shutter speeds will be a blurred image at the edges of Moon's disk.

5. You can photo the diamond ring and Baily's beads again as the eclipse ends, if you have film left.

A final word of warning is due. It's easy to forget and look through the viewfinder of a camera at the Sun. Except during totality, take care that a safe filter is fitted before you look through the viewfinder.

Videotaping

Recording the eclipse using a camcorder is really easy, and captures the full ambience of the event in sound and vision. As with photography a tripod is recommended. An ND 5 filter should be fitted throughout the partial phase, but removed as soon as the first diamond ring appears. This should be left off throughout totality and replaced about 5 seconds after the second diamond ring appears.

Most camcorders have a zoom facility and it's best to zoom right in on the Sun's image. The focal lengths of these zooms are usually not so great as to generate an image of the Sun that will be too large. Some camcorders are very light sensitive, and you may wish to consider fitting an ND 0.9 filter during totality as this can enhance the observed structure of the corona and prominences. Also, if your camcorder has a time-lapse facility, this can be used to record the partial phase, but should be switched off several minutes before totality. As with photography, it's good idea to throw a dark cloth over the instrument when you're not recording, to protect it from the heat.

Practicing

Do this at least once and as much as possible before the event to get yourself familiar with what you want to do. The times involved from start to end of totality are short, and the excitement of the event will make it difficult to think about what you are doing. Determining more exact exposure times for totality can be achieved by taking shots of the full Moon, which is roughly as bright as the solar corona, with varying speeds and apertures. Note the aperture and speed of your best exposures and use these. If you intend to use a filter during totality, remember to also use this during your test shots of the full Moon.

The same is true of videotaping. You can use the full Moon to see if you need to use a manual shutter speed (if your camcorder can do that), or to check if you need to use a filter for recording the corona.

One other piece of advice worth noting concerns the subject of light pollution. Lights from a town or road network can be so bright that they illuminate the sky. Ignore this at your peril. You may think you've found the perfect spot in a field, but when darkness comes and all the street lights automatically come on in the nearby town or motorway and light up the sky, you can put your camera down. It would be a good idea to check your chosen observing site beforehand if you can.

Finally, whether you are photographing or videotaping, ensure that you have sufficient film, tapes and charged batteries on the day!

Please note that references to filter density in the text, e.g. neutral density 5, or ND 5, refer to the filter's *optical density*. For solar photography and videorecording, only use filters made specifically for safe solar viewing. These should have an optical density of at least 4.5.

The eclipse around the world

The maximum period of totality for the 1999 eclipse will be at 11:03 GMT near Rimnicu-Vilcea to the north-west of Bucharest in Romania, and will last 2m 23s.

If you feel that the weather is too risky in north-west Europe you can venture further afield. According to the NASA Bulletin by Anderson & Espenak, the best chance of seeing the eclipse is in Esfahan, Iran, with a 95% probability. The list below gives the main countries through which the total eclipse passes, and an approximate probability of seeing the eclipse there.

England	45%
France, Belgium, Luxembourg	45-50%
Germany, Austria	50-55%
Hungary, Yugoslavia	55-60%
Romania, Bulgaria	60-65%
Turkey	65-85%
Iraq, Iran	85%-95%
Pakistan	60%-85%
India	35% or less

The traveller from Britain will find no great (statistical) advantage in France, except for the ability to move further afield more easily ahead of the eclipse, say to Germany if the weather prospects there are much better. Travelling across through Germany and Austria the prospect of clear skies increases. Continuing south-eastwards through the Balkan states, the Mediterranean dominated climate offers the best eclipse conditions in Europe this side of the Black Sea, and gets my vote. No doubt, many eclipse watchers will be drawn to this region from around the world.

Note that all further timings below are given in GMT. You will need to adjust times to local times according to the country's own conventions, as described in table 9 below.

Figure 1. Eclipse path in Europe

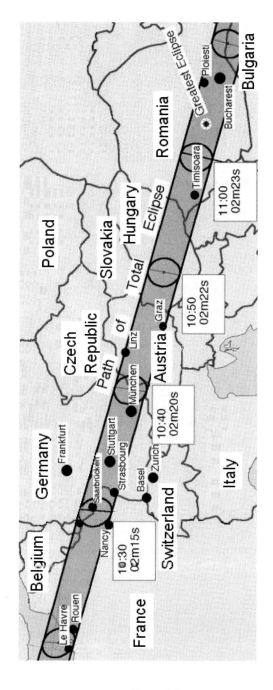

The most attractive sites are probably around Lake Balaton in Hungary (for picturesque towns and lakeside resorts), Bucharest in Romania (for ease of access, creature comforts, culture and long duration of totality), and the Romanian and Bulgarian tourist resorts along the western coast of the Black Sea.

The prospects at the resorts of Lake Balaton and the Black Sea are enhanced by the sea breezes, which should help reduce the onset of some types of cloud formation.

Totality will occur at Lake Balaton at approximately 10:50 GMT, and last for 2 minutes 22 seconds. Bucharest (11:06) will also enjoy 2m 22s of totality, which is close to the maximum of 2m 23s, near Rimnicu-Vilcea (11:03) to the north-west of Bucharest.

Table 5. Eclipse times in Hungary (in GMT)

Location	1st Contact Partial Eclipse Begins	2nd Contact Total Eclipse Begins	3rd Contact Total Eclipse Ends	4th Contact Partial Eclipse Ends	Maximum Totality	Length of Totality
Ajka	09:25:38	10:48:07	10:50:27	12:12:13	10:49:17	2m 20s
Baja	09:27:58	10:51:55	10:52:56	12:15:37	10:52:26	1m 01s
Dombóvár	09:26:34	10:50:23	10:51:13	12:14:04	10:50:48	0m 50s
Dunaújváros	09:27:58	10:50:51	10:52:50	12:14:33	10:51:51	1m 58s
Kalocsa	09:28:01	10:51:04	10:53:23	12:15:11	10:52:13	2m 19s
Kecskemét	09:29:15	10:52:31	10:53:55	12:15:46	10:53:13	1m 25s
Keszthely	09:25:05	10:48:03	10:49:52	12:12:11	10:48:57	1m 49s
Kiskunfélegyháza	09:29:32	10:52:40	10:54:39	12:16:17	10:53:39	1m 59s
Kiskunhalas	09:28:55	10:52:03	10:54:24	12:16:07	10:53:14	2m 21s
Körmend	09:24:03	10:46:37	10:48:43	12:10:52	10:47:40	2m 06s
Köszeg	09:23:59	10:46:10	10:48:29	12:10:18	10:47:19	2m 19s
Makó	09:30:39	10:53:58	10:56:21	12:17:55	10:55:10	2m 23s
Paks	09:27:51	10:50:46	10:53:09	12:14:53	10:51:57	2m 22s
Pápa	09:25:29	10:47:57	10:50:00	12:11:48	10:48:59	2m 03s
Sárvár	09:24:37	10:46:56	10:49:17	12:11:06	10:48:07	2m 20s
Siófok	09:26:28	10:49:08	10:51:30	12:13:17	10:50:19	2m 22s
Sopron	09:24:07	10:46:31	10:47:57	12:10:00	10:47:14	1m 27s
Szeged	09:30:03	10:53:22	10:55:43	12:17:22	10:54:32	2m 21s
Székesfehérvár	09:27:04	10:49:55	10:51:33	12:13:25	10:50:44	1m 37s
Szekszárd	09:27:32	10:51:01	10:52:41	12:15:00	10:51:51	1m 39s
Szentes	09:30:14	10:53:30	10:55:20	12:16:58	10:54:25	1m 50s
Szombathely	09:24:06	10:46:23	10:48:44	12:10:37	10:47:34	2m 22s
Várpalota	09:26:37	10:49:19	10:51:13	12:13:01	10:50:16	1m 54s
Veszprém	09:26:13	10:48:48	10:51:03	12:12:47	10:49:55	2m 15s
Zalaegerszeg	09:24:25	10:47:18	10:49:04	12:11:27	10:48:11	1m 46s

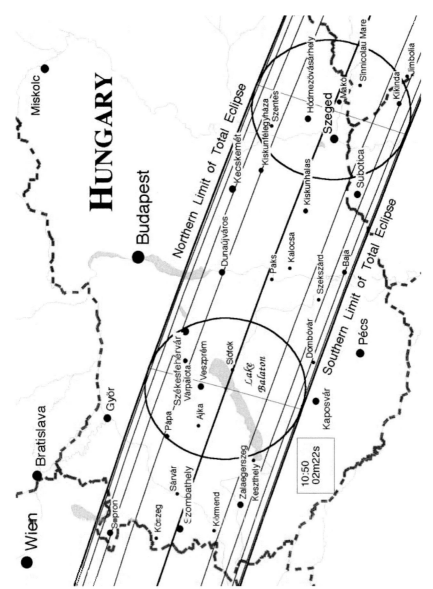

Figure 12. Eclipse path in Hungary

Table 6. Eclipse times in Romania
(in GMT)

Location	1st Contact Partial Eclipse Begins	2nd Contact Total Eclipse Begins	3rd Contact Total Eclipse Ends	4th Contact Partial Eclipse Ends	Maximum Totality	Length of Totality
Arad	09:32:09	10:55:35	10:57:49	12:19:13	10:56:42	2m 14s
Bucharest	09:41:24	11:05:47	11:08:10	12:28:43	11:06:58	2m 22s
Calarasi	09:43:52	11:08:19	11:10:34	12:30:47	11:09:27	2m 16s
Caransebes	09:33:52	10:58:01	10:59:58	12:21:40	10:58:59	1m 57s
Curtea-De-Arges	09:38:29	11:02:34	11:04:48	12:25:38	11:03:41	2m 14s
Deva	09:35:02	10:58:54	11:00:41	12:21:58	10:59:48	1m 47s
Dragasani	09:37:52	11:02:39	11:04:14	12:25:47	11:03:27	1m 34s
Hateg	09:35:09	10:58:57	11:01:17	12:22:26	11:00:07	2m 20s
Hunedoara	09:35:02	10:58:48	11:00:59	12:22:09	10:59:54	2m 10s
Jimbolia	09:31:07	10:55:08	10:56:46	12:18:53	10:55:57	1m 38s
Lipova	09:32:45	10:56:16	10:58:30	12:19:52	10:57:23	2m 15s
Lugoj	09:33:15	10:57:01	10:59:19	12:20:48	10:58:10	2m 18s
Lupeni	09:35:42	10:59:39	11:02:01	12:23:12	11:00:50	2m 22s
Mangalia	09:46:28	11:11:02	11:13:05	12:33:00	11:12:03	2m 03s
Moreni	09:40:19	11:04:40	11:06:24	12:27:11	11:05:32	1m 45s
Petrila	09:36:03	10:59:56	11:02:17	12:23:21	11:01:06	2m 21s
Petrosani	09:35:58	10:59:52	11:02:14	12:23:20	11:01:03	2m 23s
Pitesti	09:38:55	11:03:07	11:05:29	12:26:19	11:04:18	2m 23s
Ploiesti	09:41:04	11:05:34	11:07:00	12:27:49	11:06:17	1m 26s
Rîmnicu-Vîlcea	09:37:54	11:01:58	11:04:21	12:25:15	11:03:10	2m 22s
Sînnicolau Mare	09:30:55	10:54:23	10:56:42	12:18:20	10:55:32	2m 19s
Slobozia	09:43:47	11:08:56	11:09:12	12:30:13	11:09:04	0m 16s
Timisoara	09:32:00	10:55:52	10:57:54	12:19:41	10:56:53	2m 02s
Tîrgoviste	09:39:59	11:04:11	11:06:19	12:27:01	11:05:16	2m 08s
Tîrgu-Jiu	09:35:55	11:00:24	11:02:11	12:23:48	11:01:17	1m 46s
Urziceni	09:42:17	11:06:51	11:08:19	12:28:58	11:07:35	1m 28s
Vulcan	09:35:49	10:59:45	11:02:08	12:23:16	11:00:56	2m 23s

Table 7. Eclipse times in Bulgaria
(in GMT)

Location	1st Contact Partial Eclipse Begins	2nd Contact Total Eclipse Begins	3rd Contact Total Eclipse Ends	4th Contact Partial Eclipse Ends	Maximum Totality	Length of Totality
Balcik	09:45:55	11:10:51	11:12:52	12:33:10	11:11:52	2m 02s
Dobric	09:45:11	11:10:02	11:12:08	12:32:29	11:11:05	2m 05s
Isperih	09:43:10	11:08:31	11:09:44	12:30:53	11:09:08	1m 13s
Kavarna	09:46:14	11:11:04	11:13:14	12:33:23	11:12:09	2m 10s
Silistra	09:43:47	11:08:14	11:10:35	12:30:49	11:09:24	2m 21s
Tutrakan	09:42:35	11:07:15	11:09:26	12:30:03	11:08:20	2m 10s

The eastward path of the eclipse through Turkey and the Middle East offers the highest probability of clear skies on eclipse day. Beyond Turkey the difficult political situation makes the prospects less attractive. Pakistan offers reasonable prospects, but approaching India and through to the Bay of Bengal, the monsoon season will make eclipse watching much less viable than in England.

Figure 13. Eclipse path in Romania and Bulgaria

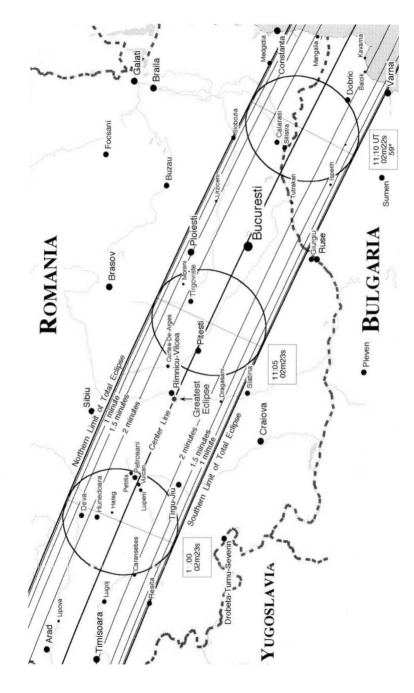

Travelling to Hungary, Romania or Bulgaria

Eclipse chasers who are tempted by the Balkans should contact their travel agents or a tour operator. Book early to avoid disappointment! There are a number of tour operators for the region, some of which are doing eclipse specials. See addendum for advice on the Yugoslavian crisis.

The main tour operators are:

Danube Travel	0171 724 7577
Fregata Travel	0171 940 1700
Budapest Breaks	0171 831 7626
Balkan Holidays	0171 543 5566
Crystal Holidays	0181 399 5144

Charity trip with Link Romania

There is an eclipse trip in Romania organised by a UK charity, Link Romania, in the form of a sponsored trek. The viewing location is Papusa in the Carpathian Alps at over 1,800m altitude, giving a very good chance of visibility, and with a maximum totality of 2m 23s. The fee is £175 if you make a commitment to raise £1500, and if you raise over £2000 then the fee is refunded. The trek runs from 5th - 12th August. Other tours are also available.

For details, contact Ann Walsh on 01903 529333, or see Link Romania web site at http://www.linkrom.org/

Visas

Visas are required for Romania and Bulgaria, though some tour operators will issue visas as part of the package. Visas are no longer required for Hungary. Further details on visa applications can also be obtained from the tourist information offices/embassies below.

Romania

Romanian Tourist Information
83a Marylebone High St
London W1

Tel: 0171 224 3692

Romanian Embassy
Arundale House
4 Palace Green
London W8 4QD

Tel: 0171 937 9666

Hungary

Hungarian Tourist Information
46 Eaton Place
London SW1

Tel: 0171 823 1032

Hungarian Embassy
46 Eaton Place
London SW1

Tel: 0171 235 5218

Bulgaria

Bulgarian Embassy
186 Queen's Gate
London SW7

Tel: 0171 584 9400

Table 8. Eclipse times around the world (in GMT)

Location		2nd Contact Total Eclipse Begins	3rd Contact Total Eclipse Ends	Maximum Totality	Length of Totality
England	Hugh Town	10:09:42	10:11:23	10:10:32	1m 41s
	Plymouth	10:12:54	10:14:32	10:13:43	1m 39s
France	Le Havre	10:18:48	10:20:20	10:19:34	1m 31s
	Metz	10:27:55	10:30:09	10:29:02	2m 13s
Belgium	Virton	10:27:07	10:28:56	10:28:01	1m 49s
Luxembourg	Luxembourg	10:28:21	10:29:41	10:29:01	1m 20s
Germany	Stuttgart	10:32:55	10:35:12	10:34:03	2m 17s
	Munich	10:37:12	10:39:20	10:38:16	2m 08s
Austria	Graz	10:44:56	10:46:09	10:45:33	1m 12s
Hungary	Szeged	10:53:22	10:55:43	10:54:32	2m 21s
Yugoslavia	Subotica	10:52:55	10:54:36	10:53:46	1m 42s
Romania	Bucharest	11:05:47	11:08:10	11:06:58	2m 22s
Bulgaria	Dobric	11:10:02	11:12:08	11:11:05	2m 05s
Turkey	Sivas	11:31:03	11:33:10	11:32:07	2m 07s
	Diyarbakir	11:39:22	11:40:42	11:40:02	1m 20s
Iraq	Irbil	11:47:25	11:49:15	11:48:20	1m 50s
	As-Sulaymaniyah	11:50:20	11:52:16	11:51:18	1m 56s
Iran	Borujerd	11:57:16	11:59:09	11:58:13	1m 53s
	Esfahan	12:02:41	12:04:15	12:03:28	1m 33s
Pakistan	Karachi	12:25:56	12:27:09	12:26:32	1m 13s
India	Baroda	12:31:05	12:32:07	12:31:36	1m 02s

Table 9. Time conversions for eclipse around the world

Location	Local Time
France	GMT + 2 hrs
Belgium	GMT + 1 hr
Luxembourg	GMT + 1 hr
Germany	GMT + 1 hr
Austria	GMT + 1 hr
Hungary	GMT + 1 hr
Romania	GMT + 2 hrs
Bulgaria	GMT + 2 hrs
Turkey	GMT + 2 hrs
Iraq	GMT + 3 hrs
Iran	GMT + 3.5 hrs
Pakistan	GMT + 5 hrs
India	GMT + 5.5 hrs

The eclipse on the Internet

For those readers with access to the Internet, the World Wide Web has several interesting pages devoted to the 1999 eclipse.

Recommended sites

Joint Organisation for Solar Observations
http://joso.oat.ts.astro.it/

NASA solar and lunar eclipse information
http://planets.gsfc.nasa.gov/eclipse/eclipse.html

NASA 1999 solar eclipse page
http://planets.gsfc.nasa.gov/eclipse/TSE1999/TSE1999.html

Link Romania - sponsored eclipse treks in Romania
http://www.linkrom.org/

Weather related sites

Sites displaying satellite images and forecasting:

http://www.tvweather.com
http://208.134.241.135/weather/sat/euro-africasat_450x284.html
http://wxp.atms.purdue.edu/
http://www.meteo.fr/tpsreel/images/satt0.jpg

Glossary of terms

1st Contact

The point at which the partial eclipse begins. The Moon begins to obscure the Sun's disk.

2nd Contact

The point at which the total eclipse begins. The first point in time during the eclipse that the Sun's disk is completely obscured by the Moon.

3rd Contact

The point at which the total eclipse ends. The Sun's disk begins to reappear from behind the Moon.

4th Contact

The time at which the partial eclipse ends. No part of the Sun's disk is any longer obscured by the Moon.

Annular eclipse

An eclipse of the Sun when the Moon appears slightly smaller than the Sun. Observed as a thin ring of the Sun's photosphere surrounding the Moon.

Baily's beads

An effect observed at the moments before and after totality during a solar eclipse where the thin crescent of the Sun is broken up into beads of light by the mountains of the Moon's surface. Named after the English astronomer Francis Baily who first pointed out the phenomenon at the solar eclipse of 1836.

Chromosphere

Gaseous layer of the Sun's outer atmosphere above the photosphere.

Corona

Sun's outermost atmosphere seen as a pearly white halo during a total eclipse.

Diamond ring

Just before (and after) totality during a solar eclipse the last (and first) glimpse of the the Sun's bright photosphere glitters like a sparkling jewel. Effectively, this is a single Baily's bead seen as a shaft of light shining through a valley on the Moon's surface.

Eclipse

An eclipse occurs when the light from one celestial body is obscured by another.

Photosphere

The brilliant visible layer of the Sun's surface.

Prominence

The flame-like structures that appear in the Sun's chromosphere and corona.

Light pollution

An effect whereby the lights from urbanised areas or motorways light up the sky at night, usually seen as a reddish/pinkish sky. Good observing conditions for astronomy (including eclipses) require low levels of light pollution.

Lunar eclipse

The light from the Sun is obscured by the Earth, as seen from the Moon - in other words, the Earth casts its shadow onto the Moon.

Partial eclipse

The stage of an eclipse where one celestial body only partly obscures the light from another. A total solar eclipse is always accompanied by a partial stage before and after totality.

Shadow bands

An effect sometimes observed during a total solar eclipse. Bands of shadow a few centimetres wide and a metre apart may be seen moving quickly across the ground moments before and after totality. Thought to be caused by lensing effects in the Earth's atmosphere, where the Sun's thin crescent is bent and focused onto the Earth's surface.

Solar eclipse

A complete or partial occultation of the Sun by the Moon, as seen from the Earth.

Total eclipse

The complete obscuration of one celestial body by another.

Transition zone

The region in the Sun's outer atmosphere between the chromosphere and corona, marking a rapid rise in temperature.

Addendum

The crisis in Yugoslavia

Since writing this book, the crisis in Yugoslavia has arisen. At the time of going to press, the Foreign Office are giving the following advice to British Nationals travelling to Hungary, Bulgaria or Romania.

The good news is that, at present, they are not advising against visiting any of these countries. They do advise taking extra care if travelling in the areas clo~~ to the border with Yugoslavia. In Romania, they advise avoiding th   ~goslavian border altogether, and that in these areas the airports of '   ~ra, Arad and Caransebes are now closed.

Contact the Foreign Offic   ~fore travelling to the Balkans in August, on 0171 23:   'heir web site at http://www.fco.gov.uk/.